Purim

A JOYOUS HOLIDAY

by Sophia N. Cedarbaum

Pictures by Clare & John Ross

Union of American Hebrew Congregations

PURIM

A JOYOUS HOLIDAY

"IT seems funny to be bringing noise-makers to the temple," giggles Debbie.

"Hush," whispers Danny. "Even though we have noisemakers, this *is* the temple. We should be quiet until we are told what to do."

It is Purim.

Debbie, her twin brother, Danny, and their parents are entering the synagogue for the Purim service.

The sanctuary is crowded with boys and girls and their mothers and fathers. Danny and Debbie's parents look around for a place where they can all sit together. There is room up in

front. They walk down the aisle and take their seats.

The rabbi tells the boys and girls what they are to do.

They are to listen as the *megillah* is being read.

He holds up the megillah so that all may see it.

The megillah is the Scroll of the Book of Esther. It is the part of the Bible that tells the Purim story.

He tells them, also, that each time they hear the name *Haman* they are to twirl their *graggers* and noisemakers as hard as they can.

The boys and girls find it strange to be told to make noise in the synagogue, but they know that on Purim this noise has a special meaning. It is a way of saying a happy "thank you" to God for keeping our Jewish people alive through the ages.

The rabbi opens the service. He asks the boys and girls to join him in reciting the blessing for the reading of the megillah.

BORUCH ATO ADONOY ELOHENU
MELECH HO-OLOM
ASHER KID'SHONU B'MITSVOSOV
V'TSIVONU AL MIKRO MEGILLAH.

BLESSED ARE YOU, O LORD OUR
GOD, KING OF THE WORLD,
WHO HAS MADE US HOLY BY
YOUR COMMANDMENTS AND
COMMANDED US TO READ THE
MEGILLAH.

The rabbi reads the first words of the megillah:

'Vay-hi bi-yme Ahasuerus. . . ."

The children listen closely for the name *Haman.*

The rabbi reads about King Ahasuerus . . . how he was angry with Queen Vashti . . . how he punished her.

But still no mention of *Haman!*

The rabbi reads on . . . "Esther, the cousin of Mordecai, the Jew, was chosen to be the new queen."

And still no mention of *Haman*! Can the rabbi be reading the wrong story?

The rabbi pauses. He looks around at the boys and girls. With a little smile he continues:

"After these things did King Ahasuerus promote Haman . . ."

What a burst of noise! The graggers go round and round. The boys and girls twirl them as hard as they can. The rattling, clacking sound of the noisemakers fills the temple!

At a signal from the rabbi the children

settle down quickly to listen for the next mention of *Haman*.

"And all the king's servants bowed down before Haman. . . . But Mordecai would not bow . . . then was Haman full of anger. . . ."

Haman went to the king. He told the king that the Jews did not obey the king's laws.

"They should be punished, all of them," said Haman to the king. And he received the king's permission to punish all the Jews in the kingdom.

When Mordecai heard of Haman's wicked plan he sent a message to Queen Esther:

"Help your people! Only you can save them!"

Esther went to the king.

The king grew very angry when he learned how Haman had tricked him . . . when he learned that his queen and her people were in danger.

He ordered Haman to be punished at once.

How happy the Jews were! They had a big celebration! They danced in the streets! They sent gifts to each other!

Since that day the Jews have celebrated Purim with fun and gladness, sending presents to each other and gifts to the poor.

The megillah reading is over. The rabbi puts the megillah back into its case.

The rabbi asks the children to rise for the closing prayer. This prayer was written by the boys and girls of the Confirmation class. The pupils of the Confirmation class step up to the pulpit to lead in the prayer.

"Dear Lord, our God, we thank You for

the privilege of celebrating this very happy and joyous festival.

"All through the years, in many different lands, cruel men, like Haman, have plotted to hurt the Jews.

"But You came to our aid and saved us from those who would do harm to Your people, Israel.

"Now, we live in a land of freedom where Hamans are not permitted to endanger the lives of any of its citizens.

"We pray that never again shall cruel Hamans rise to plot against people anywhere in the world.

"May we, like Mordecai and Esther, show courage and loyalty to You, our God; to our Torah and its teachings; and to our people, Israel.

"Amen."

Danny likes to bake. He especially likes to help his mother make *homontaschen* for Purim. He is an expert at folding the corners so that the filling does not drip out.

Debbie and Danny fill trays with these tasty Purim cakes. The trays are Purim gifts for their grandparents, aunts, uncles, and cousins. They pile the plates high. They make sure that each tray has its share of Danny's Delicious Home-Made Homontaschen. They fill in the empty spaces with nuts and raisins.

One tray is larger than the others. Danny and Debbie prepare this tray for the boys and girls of the Children's Ward of the City Hospital.

Purim afternoon their mother drives them on their rounds. They deliver the trays. At each stop their relatives give them Purim "gelt" for themselves and a tray of goodies for the family.

"This is certainly a delicious way to celebrate a holiday," exclaims Debbie, as they arrive home.

Debbie and Danny invite their friends to a Purim party. The guests are asked to come dressed in a costume.

Debbie sends invitations written on little masks to remind everyone to wear a mask.

Even the decorations for the party look like masks.

Debbie and Danny paint faces on balloons. They put long crepe paper beards on the balloons that are supposed to be Mordecai, King Ahasuerus, and Haman. They put crowns on the balloons that are supposed to be the queen.

Debbie and Danny dress in their favorite costumes.

Debbie wears a Dutch costume her aunt brought her from Holland.

Danny likes being an American cowboy.

They greet their guests at the door of the house.

Who can this be coming up the walk?

The mask is gold. The full blue robe comes almost to the ground and is covered with many beautiful stars. Maybe this is Miss Universe.

Look, here is Queen Esther. She is dressed in white. She is wearing a diamond crown.

Here comes Mordecai. He is dressed in royal purple robes. But isn't this funny? He is riding a hobby horse.

Who is that sour-faced man leading him? It is probably Haman. Now, who do you think would want to be Haman?

The house is soon full of loud laughter as each child tries to guess who the other children are.

Debbie and Danny have a special treat for their friends this year.

Uncle David will show them his movies of "Purim in Tel Aviv." Uncle David is a very jolly man. He is full of fun. When he describes his films he makes you feel as though you are right there with him watching the Purim celebration.

"Step right up, ladies and gentlemen," calls Uncle David. "You are about to see the world's most exciting show: 'The Adloyada in Tel Aviv.' "

"What is the *Adloyada?*"

"Why, it is a parade, a Purim parade, a very colorful Purim parade. It is miles long and lasts for hours.

"From early morning people have been gathering for the parade.

"No one wants to miss the fun!

"Here is a picture showing the crowds.

"Here comes the parade! Trucks! Wagons! Marchers! Bands of muscians!

"The trucks are decorated. Some trucks are flat so that boys and girls in costumes can act out a scene.

"Each scene shows something special about Israel, about the Bible, or about the Purim story.

"Yes, I agree with you," says Uncle David, as the boys and girls "oh" and "ah" at the next picture. "This is a lovely sight. These are fifth grade girls dressed as Persian dancers. They are entertaining Queen Esther.

"And here comes the queen. She is sitting on her throne, surrounded by her ladies-in-waiting. She smiles and waves at the people watching the parade.

"Let's give a big cheer for Queen Esther,

the beautiful queen who saved her people."

The children gladly join Uncle David in a loud cheer.

"Heydad! Heydad! Hurrah! Hurrah!"

The lights go on. The children applaud Uncle David and his films.

"Let's play some games now," calls Debbie. Soon all the children are playing. They play "Pin the Crown on Queen Esther," "Going to Shushan" and "Purim Bingo."

Then they gather around the piano. Debbie's mother plays and the children sing. They know many Purim songs.

They sing:

> This is Purim fellows,
> A joyous holiday. . . .

They sing:

> Oh, once there was a wicked, wicked
> man,
> And Haman was his name, sir. . . .

They sing:

> Purim's here, Purim cheer,
>   'Tis a holiday so dear. . . .

While their guests are singing, Debbie and Danny disappear into the kitchen.

When they come back Danny is wearing a high cook's hat and a white apron. He is carrying a tray of homontaschen. He is very proud to offer his guests his own Danny's Delicious Home-Made Homontaschen. The boys and girls smack their lips and say that these are the best homontaschen they have ever eaten.

Debbie serves fruit punch.

Everyone has a wonderful time at the party.

We hope that you, too, will have a HAPPY PURIM!